Two Dads

Written by Carolyn Robertson

Illustrated by Sophie Humphreys

Published 2014 by Sparklypoo Publications London UK

www.sparklypoo.com

For Vinnie

Not everyone I meet or see is even half as lucky as me.

For I have something that can't be bad... I don't have one...

I have two Dads!

Dads, Daddies, Papas, Pops.

Or fathers if you'd rather (but I think that sounds quite posh!)

Dads come in every shape and size.

One of mine's tall, the other has brown eyes.

I didn't come out of either
Dad's tummy.

I wasn't dropped by a stork...

or found by a bunny

No, I am rather special you see...

both my Dads adopted me!

My Dads like driving me to school.

My friends think both my Dads are cool.

Dads are very good at chasing, ducking, diving and high speed racing. They can't be beaten at pushing swings...

Or on trampolines or vertical rings....

My Dads can cook delicious dinners.

Their pizza toppings are always winners.

Their birthday cakes are the best I've ever tasted.

And in our house not a crumb gets wasted.

Weekends with Dads are never boring,

cos even if one's tired and snoring...

There's another Dad always ready to play.

For a whizz around the park or a swim if it's grey.

Having two Dads means double the fun.

Double sets of shoulders for me to rest upon.

Double sets of big strong arms, to pick me up if I get hurt.

And twice as many clean shirt sleeves, to wipe my nose of snot and dirt.

At the end of the day when I'm bathed and well-fed.

I can choose which Daddy puts me to bed.

But sometimes I find it too hard to decide.

I'm not sure which Dad I want by my side.

I want two Daddy stories and two Daddy cuddles.

Two Daddy smiles and two Daddy snuggles.

Yes what I love best when I turn off the light...

Is both Daddies kiss me and whisper

"Night night"

About The Author

Carolyn and her partner are adoptive Mums to two fabulous boys. Carolyn is a school teacher and author. She lives and works in South London.

CPSIA information can be obtained
at www.ICGtesting.com
Printed in the USA
LVHW071522181121
703739LV00009B/313